The Dormouse

by Paul Bright & Pat Morris

CONTENTS

The Dormouse

The dormouse is one of the most distinctive small mammals native to Britain. It is now rare and apparently declining and its nocturnal and hibernating habits have shrouded the dormouse in mystery. Recent research, reviewed in this booklet, reveals the highly complex ecology of this fascinating animal and suggests ways to assist its conservation.

Appearance

The dormouse (*Muscardinus avellanarius*) is an attractive species, easily distinguished from all other small mammals by its thick furry tail, sandy pelage and bulging black eyes. It is about 70mm long, with a tail of similar length. Normal body weights are around 17g, with juveniles at half this size - dormice weigh more at the start of hibernation, sometimes as much as 40g.

	Normal weight g	Weight before hibernation g	Weight after hibernation g
Adult (60-90mm)	15-22	25-40	15-20
Juvenile (40-50mm)	7-14	18-28	12-16
Pregnant female	26 max	-	-

Sizes of dormice according to age and time of year.

Young dormice tend to be greyer than adults which are a sandy-yellow colour. Dormice have a white chest patch and about 10% of the population show a white tail-tip. Albinos do occur but are very rare. Dormice have many pads on the soles of their feet which assist in gripping tree branches and small twigs among which the animals are active.

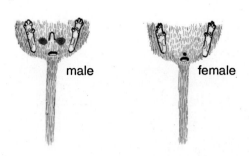

male female

Male and Female. Note separation between openings in male and female, also testes that are obvious only during the breeding season.

Both fore and hind feet are prehensile (gripping) and the hind feet can be turned backwards (like those of a squirrel). This allows a dormouse to hang head down to feed on flowers and fruits and also to run head first down tree trunks. Male and female dormice are less easy to distinguish than the sexes of mice and voles, as the males do not develop very prominent testes in the breeding season.

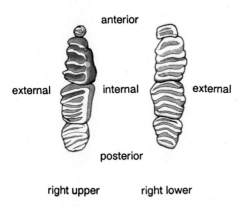

The characteristic teeth ridges of a dormouse.

The skull of a dormouse looks like that of other rodents, Except that there are four molar teeth (instead of the three seen in rats, mice and voles), each of which has many parallel distinct cross ridges. These and other features allow dormice to be classified in a separate rodent family, the Gliridae, of which *Muscardinus* is the only native British member. A second species, the fat or edible dormouse (*Glis glis*) was introduced to England in 1902 and today is fairly numerous, but only in the woodlands in the Tring/ Wendover/ Berkhamstead area. This species resembles a small grey squirrel and is approximately 10 times the size of *Muscardinus*.

Signs

Dormice are small, nocturnal and tree-living and so are unlikely to be seen, even by determined observers. Their presence is usually indicated by finding characteristic signs.

Dormouse nests may be discovered, particularly by careful inspection of bramble and other low-growing shrubs. Each is about the size of a grapefruit and made of woven stripped bark (occasionally grass) surrounded by outer layers of leaves. It looks similar to

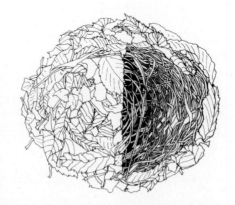

Nest structure. The inner layer is woven bark, occasionally grass. The outer layer is made of concentrically arranged leaves.

Even inside a nestbox, the dormouse makes a woven nest from fibrous material.

a wren's nest, but lacks a "doorstep" or obvious entrance and usually lack of moss. These nests are used in summer, sometimes for breeding, but are most easily seen in winter among bare twigs. However, dormice usually nest in

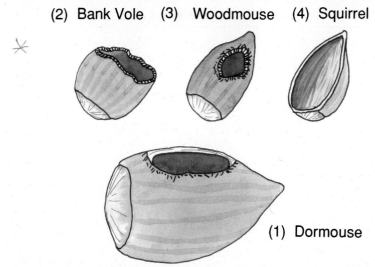

(2) Bank Vole   (3) Woodmouse   (4) Squirrel

(1) Dormouse

Gnawed hazel nut shells. (1) opened by a dormouse, there is a neat round hole with no teeth marks on the cut face, but teeth marks on the surface of the shell; (2) Bank voles bite straight across, leaving teeth marks on the cut edge but not on the shell surface; (3) Woodmice leave teeth marks on the cut face and the surface of the shell; (4) Squirrels crack nuts cleanly in half, or into jagged pieces.

tree hollows, often high above ground, where they are unlikely to be found. Nestboxes, put up for bats or birds are also used by dormice.

The presence of dormice is most likely to be discovered by searching for characteristically gnawed nuts below hazel bushes. While squirrels and birds tend to smash hazel nuts, leaving jagged pieces of shell, small rodents gnaw a neat hole. Having made a hole in the nut, a dormouse will enlarge it, using its teeth to scrape away more material with a scooping action along the cut edge of the nutshell. The cut surface thus appears smooth or has very faint tooth marks around it, dormice do also leave tooth marks on the surface of the shell, which radiate out at about 45^0 from the hole. Woodmice by contrast leave tooth marks on both the cut face and the surface of the shell.

Dormice do not normally enter standard small mammal traps (e.g. Longworths), nor are they attracted by the grain baits often used. They can be caught in specially made wire cage traps baited with apple. However, as it is a strictly protected species under the Wildlife and Countryside Act 1981, trapping for dormice must be licensed by the statutory nature conservation bodies (English Nature or the Countryside Council for Wales) otherwise a serious legal offence is committed with fines of up to £2000 per dormouse!

Honeysuckle flower, showing the fallen remains of a floret after dormice have been feeding.

Dormice will readily use special nestboxes put up for them (see below). Carefully checking these nestboxes monthly does not cause significant disturbance to the animals, but again does require a licence even if you have put up the boxes yourself on your own land.

Dormouse skulls are distinctive, but are rarely found. They form less than 1% of the prey items in owl pellets and have only twice been reported trapped in discarded bottles. Dormice themselves are occasionally caught by cats, or even found lying asleep on woodland paths!

Distribution

Because dormice are so elusive, our knowledge of distribution is very incomplete. Nevertheless, a Mammal Society Survey in the early 1980's showed a distinctly southerly distribution pattern, dormice being found mostly south of a line from the River Thames to the River Severn and in the Welsh borders. However, even within this area, most woods do not contain dormice and the species seems to be distributed very patchily.

4

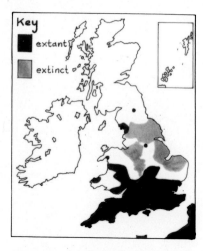

Map showing the present and former distribution of dormice in Britain.

Dormice are scarce in northern and eastern counties. This probably reflects the influence of climate, particularly the length of the winter and the frequency of cold or wet weather in summer. They may easily become extinct in a wood (see section on Conservation and Woodland management). Once the animals have been lost from isolated woods, they are unlikely to return, especially if it means dispersing over open ground. Thus, present day absence from apparently suitable sites may be an historical effect. The history of the landscape, such as the introduction of Medieval corn fields or open pastures in central England may account for the thin distribution of dormice there today. In the south and west by contrast, there is generally more woodland, which is frequently of ancient origin. Woodlands here also tend to be less isolated by open ground and are often linked by hedgerows or woodland strips which may allow recolonisation by dormice.

Habitat

In the past, dormice have most often been found in areas of coppiced hazel, perhaps partly because coppicing is labour-intensive and woodcutters are quite likely to encounter dormice. This has led to the animal being frequently referred to as the "hazel dormouse", an association reinforced by conducting distribution surveys based upon searching for gnawed hazel nuts. However, dormice are also found in other woodland habitats including areas dominated by oak and holly or birch or oak/ash woodlands. These are almost certainly poor habitats for dormice. Generally the species seems to prefer woodland edge, overgrown clearings and areas of high diversity of trees and shrubs. the best habitats for dormice seem to have a vigorous, unshaded shrub layer producing plenty of food for the animals - and some mature canopy trees. Habitats need a variety of tree species, particularly ones producing berries (e.g. wayfaring tree, blackthorn) or nuts (e.g. hazel).

The tiny radio transmitter collar worn by dormice so that their movements and feeding habits can be traced.
(Shown on a £1 coin)

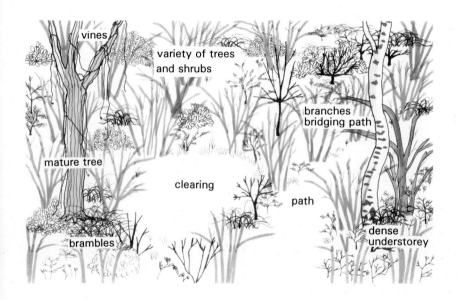

Habitat with a well developed and diverse shrub layer, plus canopy trees and vines, known to be good for dormice.

Activity and movements

Dormice are nocturnal. They leave their nests about one hour after sunset and return in the small hours or by dawn. Very occasionally, just before hibernation for example, they may be active during the day. Their movements have been studied using radio tracking, a difficult task with such a small animal, especially in the dark and in dense undergrowth.

Dormice rely heavily on their large eyes to find their way about and to navigate among the complex arboreal routeways they use in the tree canopy. They have long whiskers which help them feel their way about in dark places. Their sense of smell is very good and used to locate food and determine its ripeness, but nobody knows whether they also use it for communication as do other groups of mammals. It is possible that they communicate using ultrasound, but to the human ear only occasional squeaks or wheezing noises are heard - from the young or during arousal from torpor.

During their activity period, dormice rarely go more than 70 metres from their daytime nest and most remain within 50m of it. Males range more widely than females and the actual distances travelled per night vary with the seasons and type of food source being exploited. Dormice are active entirely in the tree and shrub layers, running and springing about the branches with great agility. They are very reluctant indeed to come to ground level or traverse open spaces, instead they will make lengthy detours in the canopy in order to use a convenient branch bridging a wide path or travel around an area of open ground.

The area they use (their "home range") is quite small, typically only 3000 square metres or so. This is compensated for by using all three dimensions of their habitat. Dormice sometimes spend a lot of time high in tall trees over 10 metres above the ground. They may pass several days and nights in the crown of a single tree without coming down at all. At other times they are active at lower levels, particularly where the shrub layer offers important foods such as hazel nuts and blackberries.

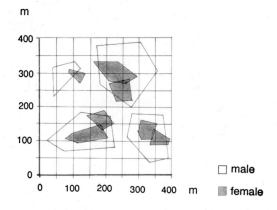

Arrangement of male and female dormouse ranges.
The larger male ranges overlap those of one or two females

In the dark it is difficult to observe dormouse behaviour. However, they do seem to be aware of each other's presence and will adopt an aggressive stance and flick their tail, just as squirrels do, to unwelcome intruders. For the most part dormice do not seem to defend territories, though males may do so during the breeding season. Males use larger areas than females and their home ranges usually overlap those of two or more females.

Some indication of social behaviour is shown by the fact that two or more dormice may be found living together in the same nestbox. In the breeding season, adult males may share a box with females, but not with another

7

adult male. Marking the animals reveals that the same pair may use the same nestbox in consecutive years, suggesting a long-term pair bond. This is a common feature of carnivore and primate species for example, but unusual among such small rodents.

Pollen from hawthorn flowers is one of the important foods sought out by dormice early in the season.

Food

The digestive system of the dormouse is anatomically ill-adapted to processing large amounts of low grade food such as leaves. Instead they are specialist feeders, concentrating on high-grade foods such as nectar, sugar-rich berries and insects. This necessitates changing their foraging habits seasonally.

Exactly what a dormouse eats depends on what is available within about 70 metres of its nest. By the time a dormouse emerges from hibernation, in late April or May, many tree catkins are already over. However, hawthorn flowers, for example, are available and the animal will move rapidly through the bushes to identify those at the optimum stage of development. It will bite off the anthers, a rich source of protein. After a couple of weeks feeding mainly in this way, the hawthorn flowers will be over and the dormouse will move to something else. This might be the flowers of honeysuckle which provide sweet and nutritious nectaries to eat.

As the summer progresses, the dormouse will move on to newly available foods. It may climb into sycamore trees for example and hang upside down to eat the dangling flowers. Later it might do the same in ash trees, nibbling at the developing seeds and dropping gnawed "keys" to the ground below. wayfaring tree, field maple and many other species contribute to the late summer diet, followed by blackberries and other fruits. When available, the dormouse will then turn to hazel nuts. The latter are eaten when ripe but still on the tree. At this stage the green shell is still relatively soft and much easier to tackle than when brown and fully hardened - the state in which they are found on the ground. The animals forage to the tips of branches, seeking suitable nuts which are then opened and eaten, a process which usually takes about 20 minutes per nut. It is probably hazel nuts which often provide the most body fat for hibernation.

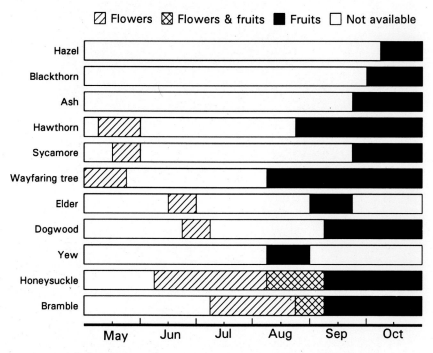

Availability of tree flowers and fruits for dormice through the summer.

This type of itinerant, arboreal foraging means that the normal activity pattern consists of short bursts spent travelling to a suitable bush or tree, followed by perhaps several hours spent among the same branches feeding mostly on the same thing. Where food is clustered and nutritious (e.g.

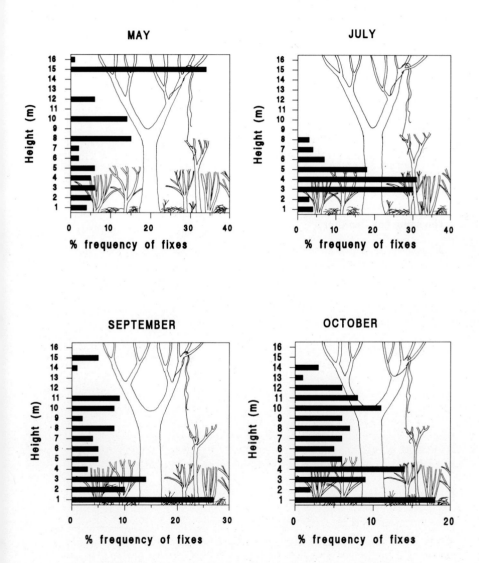

The number of times radio tracked dormice were located ("fixes") at different heights above the woodland floor at different times of the year.

bunches of wayfaring tree berries) most of the night may be spent in one place. Otherwise the animals will be forced to travel more widely and forage less efficiently.

A major problem for dormice is the period between the end of the main tree flower season and the beginning of the fruiting period. This gap in available food may last from mid June until mid August, depending upon the weather, latitude and plant species available. Honeysuckle flower's nectar and bramble flowers (providing pollen) offer some food, but there are few other species available. At this time dormice will often forage extensively in oak trees (or other species) and may well be eating a lot of caterpillars and perhaps other seasonal insects such as aphids. Faecal analysis confirms that dormice do take considerable quantities of insects during the summer. Even so, July is probably a difficult time for them.

Radio tracking shows that dormice do not travel far, perhaps because they need an

Dormice can hang head down by their back feet to reach flowers high in the tree tops.

intimate knowledge of a small area to allow discovery of patchy and ephemeral food sources. So the best habitats for dormice will be those with a high species diversity among the trees and shrubs, all thoroughly intermixed. Exactly which plant species are present is probably less important than the principle that there should be enough diversity to guarantee continuity of food through the seasons, from April to November.

Nests & Nestboxes

Dormice often build woven nests in low shrubs during the summer (see above), but radio tracking the animals shows that they also use a wide variety of other places to spend the daylight hours such as old bird nests and squirrel dreys. They also shelter in tree holes and behind loose bark, building a nest in such cavities where they are very unlikely to be found by casually searching humans or predators.

Tree hollows seem to be the dormouse's preferred nesting site, and the availability of tree holes for nesting is probably one of the factors which limit dormouse numbers. This would be particularly so in coppiced woodland where much of the growth is too thin and young to provide tree holes.

The importance of such nest sites is revealed when artificial substitutes are provided in the form of nestboxes. It has long been known that the populations of many hole-nesting birds can be boosted by offering them nestboxes to make up for a deficiency of natural tree hollows, especially in plantations and young woodland. The same appears to be true for dormice. Experiments have shown that their population density may be doubled in areas where special nestboxes are provided.

Dormice will occupy ordinary bird nestboxes (and bat boxes), but readily use specially designed dormouse boxes. These should have an entrance hole of 30mm diameter turned to face a tree trunk or big branch to provide easy access. A spacing bar above and below the entrance hole holds the box clear of the tree, leaving room for the animals to get in and out. This arrangement also makes it more difficult for birds to get in and take over the box, thereby alleviating potential competition. Occasionally both a bird and a dormouse will use the same box together!

Nestboxes will be occupied throughout the summer, and given sufficient nestboxes, it appears that nearly the entire dormouse population will learn to use them. However, they do not give up other nests entirely. Radio tracking shows that in one week a dormouse may use two or three different nests, either natural or artificial. Females will use nestboxes to raise their families as they offer a secure and weather-proof site, possibly enhancing survival of the babies.

With the first frosty nights of autumn, most dormice will desert their nestboxes and seek suitable places to hibernate on the ground. They do not use nest boxes over winter, probably because they get too dry and the inside temperature is too high and variable for efficient hibernation. Dormice found occasionally in nestboxes during winter are probably starving animals, aroused from hibernation, perhaps in a futile search for food.

Dormouse nestbox with the entrance facing the tree trunk.

Breeding and population density

Dormice hibernate until May so breeding cannot start very early in the year. They are unlikely to produce young before mid June. In years of poor food availability when bad weather has prolonged hibernation or frequently curtailed nocturnal feeding, litters may not be born until August or September. Other small woodland rodents such as mice and voles will already have raised at least one litter by this time. Young dormice may be born as late as October, but in many years it is unlikely that these late arrivals will be able to fatten up sufficiently in time to survive hibernation.

Families are small and the young remain blind, pink and helpless for the first few days after birth.

Dormice normally have small litters, typically of four or five young, but occasionally seven or eight. Large families may also be encountered in nestboxes resulting from two females combining their families in the same place. The young are born pink, blind and helpless. At about seven days they have grey fur. At about 18 days they have a grey brown fur and open their eyes. Still later their mother takes them out foraging, returning to spend the day with them in the same nest. The juveniles may remain with their mother for six or even eight weeks, very much longer than woodmice for example that are independent at about 17 days.

By spending a long time raising her family, the female dormouse probably assists their survival. However, the late start to breeding and this long period of maternal care, means that dormice can usually rear only one litter a year. Dormice might sometimes have two litters in a year, but probably do not normally manage to raise more than one. Again this contrasts with typical mice which not only have larger litters, but also raise more of them in a year. The dormouse is therefore an example of what we call a "K-strategist", with a low annual reproductive rate which is balanced by living a long time (see below).

This slow breeding pattern should not be seen as a mark of failure. Dormice are specialist feeders, occupying rare and patchy habitats. Such habitats cannot support high densities of dormice, so the dormouse strategy is to breed slowly and live at low population density. Typically, dormice live at a density of only about 8 - 10 per hectare, even in prime habitat. This is a tenth as many as woodland mice and voles.

Hibernation and annual cycle

With the onset of cold weather in October, dormice begin to hibernate. Larger animals start hibernating before lighter ones, who wait until they are fatter. Food can remain available on trees into November, so this is probably the hibernation deadline except in very mild years. Radiotracking has shown that dormice hibernate at ground level in woven nests (like summer ones) partially covered by moss or leaf litter. This descent to ground level is in marked contrast to the dormouses' arboreal life during the summer when they rarely come to the ground at all.

Hibernation in this species is profound and it is unlikely that dormice move about much during the winter. They will nevertheless arouse periodically, but do not leave their nest, unless it becomes too wet or too dry or temperature conditions in it are unfavourable. They need to avoid dryness because the animals do not drink during hibernation. If they get water at all, it is from the moss or leaf litter around the nest. In too dry a place, a

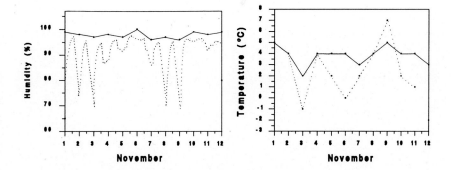

Temperature and humidity in places where dormice nest in summer and at ground level where they hibernate. Temperature and humidity are much more variable in the air (dotted lines) than they are on the ground (solid lines) where dormice hibernate.

14

Dormouse cold and curled up during hibernation.

hibernating dormouse desiccates very quickly. It is also important not to be too warm, because fat reserves get used up too soon. Cold is less of a problem, at least in Britain's relatively warm winters. Below about $2^{o}C$ the animal's metabolism will speed up to keep the body above freezing point.

A hibernator's body temperature falls to that of its surroundings and its heart and breathing rate slow down by 90% or more. In this state it needs very little energy to stay alive. This energy comes from fat reserves. It is obviously therefore important that enough fat be accumulated before winter begins in order to support the animal for five or six months of hibernation. It appears that a minimum body weight of at least 15g is necessary for winter survival in juveniles. Some of the older adults may weigh more, up to 40g when they enter hibernation, with fat comprising almost half of their mass!

Summer torpor

Hibernation is a strategy for saving energy at a time of year when food is scarce and energy costs cannot be met by going out to feed. The dormouse appears to adopt a similar strategy in the summer too. In early summer especially, food is often in short supply. Windy or wet nights may also curtail foraging. At this time, dormice will frequently enter torpor (a sort of temporary hibernation with much reduced body temperature and immobility) during the morning. This saves energy, but also contributes to delaying the onset of the breeding season. In this state, they are incapable

15

of escape if discovered. Hence the importance of a secure nest site. At this time of year they are often found in empty nestboxes - they do not need nests when torpid.

Hibernation and torpor are clearly central to the dormouse's ecology. Reduction in body temperature allows dormice to survive when food is short during the summer, as well as in winter. So dormice can spend up to half the year in hibernation and be torpid for much of the remaining time. It was this behaviour that earned dormice their sleepy reputation, characterised at the Madhatter's tea party in "Alice in Wonderland". What the dormouse probably needs most is positive seasons - consistently hot summers and cold winters. These continental conditions - experienced through most of the dormouse's range in Europe - enhance food availability in summer and provide conditions more suitable for hibernation in winter. In Britain however, the dormouse is on the western edge of its distributional range and must contend with a maritime climate to which it seems poorly suited. Cool wet summers, all too common in Britain, lead to less food being available for dormice. Mild winters may then reduce survival during hibernation, because higher temperatures and sudden warm spells cause the animals to metabolize faster or arouse from hibernation completely - so depleting their precious fat stores and reducing their chances of surviving through till May. The vagaries of the British climate probably contribute significantly to the problems faced by dormice in this country and at least partly account for its historical decline.

During summer torpor, the animals are cold and inactive. They may take twenty minutes to wake up fully.

The dormouse deserves its old name of 'sleeper': in winter it spends six months in hibernation and often goes torpid in summer too. It must spend well over half its life asleep.

Predators and mortality

Studies of *Muscardinus* in France and Germany have shown that these animals can live to be four or five years old in the wild. By contrast, typical mice or voles are lucky to survive six months and very few live more than a year. British dormice also enjoy a comparatively low mortality rate, typically 50% of adults may survive from one year into the next.

The main danger is probably being unprepared for hibernation; dormice face relatively few other threats. Among the dense leaves and twigs in the forest canopy they are fairly safe from owls. The tawny owl (a species that normally preys on woodland mammals) usually swoops from a vantage point to catch mice and voles on the ground, where dormice rarely venture. Barn owls occasionally catch dormice as they hunt along hedgerows. However, there is no predator for whom the dormouse provides more than a fraction of one percent of their prey, though weasels may in time learn to find them in nestboxes.

Dormice seem to carry fewer fleas and ticks than most other mammals - about ten individuals were found with fleas out of thousands of captures, and ticks are even more rare. There is also no evidence that parasites or disease cause significant mortality in dormouse populations.

one large wood   **two smaller woods**

same total area

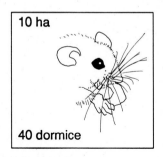

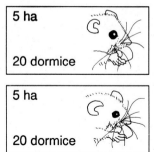

The insidious effect of fragmenting woods. Because dormice live at low density, even a quite large wood may have only a few dozen dormice. Smaller woods support dormouse populations that are each too small to be viable in the long term.

Conservation and Woodland Management

Coppicing of hazel is a traditional form of woodland management the purpose of which was to provide poles for fencing and building, for charcoal-making and other uses. The practice also generates a habitat which particularly suits the needs of the dormouse. This type of management has almost died out over the last 50 years and much coppice has now been lost to other uses including conifer plantations, farmland and road development. Lack of woodland management and complete loss of woodlands are probably the main reason for dormouse decline.

Abandoned coppice becomes dark and shady, loses its understorey and supports fewer dormice. However, reinstatement of coppicing, as proposed and practised by many conservationists may also be very damaging to dormice. This is because large patches (more than 0.5ha) are often cut and the coppice is then not allowed sufficient time to re-grow to be useful to dormice, before it is cut again. It commonly takes 7 - 10 years for shrubs to be sufficiently mature to produce much food for dormice, so coppice rotations of 15 - 20 years (depending on local circumstances) are best for them. Often coppice is cut on a much shorter rotation than this so that a large proportion of a wood may be too young to provide the flowers, nuts and fruits needed to support dormice. Large cleared areas also mean that dormice have to make detours through shrubs and trees to reach sources of food. Thus coppicing to benefit dormice needs to be done in small patches (less than 0.3 ha) and on long rotations. Otherwise there is a risk that too much of a wood will be made unsuitable for the animals and their local extinction precipitated. In many nature reserves, coppice is cut on a short rotation because this provides visible improvement to the flowers and butterflies; the damage done to dormice is easily overlooked.

Dormice prefer woods where mature trees are widely spaced, between which plenty of sunlight can stimulate vigorous growth of a species rich understorey. Mature trees including oak, ash and sycamore can be important sources of food. However, if such woods are coppiced in large patches, many of the mature trees will be left isolated, surrounded by open ground which dormice do not like to cross. It is better to leave some shrubs between the trees to provide access to them. Wide paths or tracks can usefully be bridged by leaving overhanging branches, every 50m or so.

From what has been said earlier it is obvious that putting up nestboxes is also a useful conservation-management activity. They should be put out in groups of at least 10 boxes within 15 - 20 metres of each other, not on isolated trees. They are best set at about 1.5 - 2 metres above ground level. However, it is very important that they are not put up where they may be disturbed and dormice in them put at risk. Remember a licence is required to check dormouse nestboxes. Where dormice are present at relatively high densities, nestboxes will be occupied within the first summer of availability (provided that plenty of boxes are available). Old bird nests, and any wet dormouse nests should be emptied out at the end of each winter. Dry dormouse nests should be left alone as the animals are likely to return to them in spring.

An arboreal species, the dormouse depends very much on the way that woods are managed.

A major problem for the dormouse is that many of our remaining woodland areas are too small. A five hectare copse for example, may only have 20 - 30 dormice in it. This may be too small a population to survive chance events e.g. a succession of poor breeding seasons or chance production of too few female offspring. So it is important that where small woods do still contain dormice, management operations should not reduce effective size still further, e.g. by coppicing large patches each year. If 1ha is coppiced annually, after five years this leaves 5ha of hazel still too young to supply nuts, halving the effective size of a 10ha wood from the point of view of the dormouse population. This may then leave just too few animals to form a viable population and they will die out.

These are young dormice taking rose hips.

Captive breeding and reintroduction

In most years young dormice weighing less than 12g by the end of October are very unlikely to survive hibernation. They can be taken into captivity without jeopardising the population. This must only be done under licence from English Nature or the Countryside Council for Wales. Kept indoors, warm and well fed, these animals will grow sufficiently to hibernate later in captivity and may well breed in subsequent years. However, dormice do not readily breed in captivity, perhaps because their social behaviour is distorted by keeping them in pairs or small numbers. It is also difficult to replace the wide variety of food to which they are accustomed in the wild.

Even if dormice can be bred in large numbers in captivity, or are taken from the wild, it is far from certain that a reintroduction project would succeed.

If dormice are absent from a wood, (the usual reason for a planned introduction), there must be an explanation. It would be cruel and wasteful to release dormice that were doomed to extinction due to bad habitat. It is also wasteful to release dormice into a wood without first checking thoroughly to make sure that they are not already present.

Captive-bred animals (or even experienced wild dormice translocated from another woodland area) may well not cope with release at an unfamiliar site. Food sources and nest sites need to be found in a new environment, and without travelling far, in just a few nights. Before such reintroductions are attempted, it is essential to find out exactly what the minimum necessary habitat size is, where reintroduced dormice stand the greatest chance of success and in what parts of the country the climate is most favourable to dormice. At the time of writing, much of this is unknown and a lot more research is needed. Until it is done, reintroductions are premature.

Further Reading and Sources of Information

Dormice are such elusive creatures that until recently few studies had been made of them. The work upon which this booklet is based was carried out at Royal Holloway & Bedford New College (University of London) and by The Mammal Society's Conservation Officer. Consequently there are few other sources of information, except those published before 1985 which lack much of the detail given here and are mostly now difficult to obtain. Nevertheless, the following may be helpful.

Bright, P. & Morris, P. (1989) A Practical Guide to Dormouse Conservation. *Mammal Society Occasional Publication* no.11.

Bright, P.W. and Morris, P.A. (1990) Habitat Requirements of Dormice in Relation to Woodland Management in South West England. *Biological Conservation.* 54: 307 - 326

Bright, P.W. and Morris, P.A. (1991) Ranging and Nesting Behaviour of the Dormouse (*Muscardinus avellanarius*) in Diverse Low-Growing Woodland. *Journal of Zoology* 224: 177 - 190.

Corbet, G.B. & Harris, S. (1991.) *The Handbook of British Mammals* (3rd edn.) Blackwell, Oxford.

Hurrell, E. (1980) *The Common Dormouse*. Blandford Press (*out of print*).

List of useful addresses
(from whom further information about British Mammals is available).

The Mammal Society Conservation Office, Zoology Department, University of Bristol, Woodland Road, Bristol BS8 1UG

The Vincent Wildlife Trust, 10 Lovat Lane, London EC3R 8DT

English Nature, Northminster House, Peterborough PE1 1UA

The Countryside Council for Wales, Plan Penrhos, Ffordd Penrhos, Bangor, Gwynedd LL57 2LQ